Hymns for
Occasions

Hymns for Occasions

ONE HUNDRED SPECIAL ARRANGEMENTS

Colin Mawby

Kevin
Mayhew

We hope you enjoy the music in *Hymns for Occasions*.
Further copies are available from your local music shop or Christian bookshop.

In case of difficulty, please contact the publisher direct by writing to:

The Sales Department
KEVIN MAYHEW LTD
Buxhall
Stowmarket
Suffolk IP14 3BW

Phone 01449 737978
Fax 01449 737834
E-mail info@kevinmayhewltd.com

Please ask for our complete catalogue of outstanding Church Music.

First published in Great Britain in 1994 by Kevin Mayhew Ltd.

© Copyright 1994 Kevin Mayhew Ltd.

ISBN 0 86209 568 9
Catalogue No: 1400026

2 3 4 5 6 7 8 9

Cover design by Jonathan Stroulger
Music Editor: Joanne Clarke
Music setting by Louise Hill

Contents

Foreword

The arrangements in *Hymns for Occasions* are intended for use at those times when the organist is looking for extra material to add interest and splendour to the hymn singing.

All the arrangements include an introduction, the standard harmonisation of the hymn tune, a passage which leads into a more complex last verse harmonisation, and a concluding few bars. The introduction (which always contains enough of the hymn tune to act as an encouragement to the congregation) should normally be used only before the first verse of the hymn, and subsequent verses should all end with the passage marked with a first-time bar. In the penultimate verse the organist should follow the directions marked in the second-time bar, proceeding via the linking passage into the last verse arrangement. The conclusion provides a flourish. Both the introduction and the conclusion are optional – the organist should choose to use all or part of each arrangement as befitting the occasion. The use of the pedal is assumed in the introduction, last verse and conclusion.

I hope *Hymns for Occasions* will provide yet more useful music for parish organists at a time when hymn singing is already enjoying a remarkable renaissance.

COLIN MAWBY

1 ADESTE FIDELES

2. Lead into last verse

Last verse

Refrain

Conclusion

Metre: Irregular
Melody: John Francis Wade (1711-1786)

2 ALL FOR JESUS

2. Lead into last verse

Last verse

Conclusion

Metre: 87 87
Melody: John Stainer (1840-1901)

3 ALL THINGS BRIGHT AND BEAUTIFUL

2. Lead into last verse

Last verse

Refrain

Conclusion

Metre: 76 76 and Refrain
Melody: William Henry Monk (1823-1889)

13

4 ANGEL VOICES

Last verse

Conclusion

Metre: 85 85 843
Melody: Edwin George Monk (1819-1900)

5   ANIMA CHRISTI

Last verse

Conclusion

Metre: 10 10 10 10
Melody: William Maher (1823-1877)

17

6 AR HYD Y NOS

Last verse

Conclusion

Metre: 84 84 88 84
Melody: Traditional Welsh

19

7 AURELIA

Introduction

2. Lead into last verse

Last verse

Conclusion

Metre: 76 76 D
Melody: Samuel Sebastian Wesley (1810-1876)

8 AUSTRIA

Last verse

Conclusion

Metre: 87 87 D
Melody: Croation folk tune adapted by Franz Joseph Haydn (1732-1809)

23

9 BATTLE HYMN

Refrain

1. D.S. for more verses

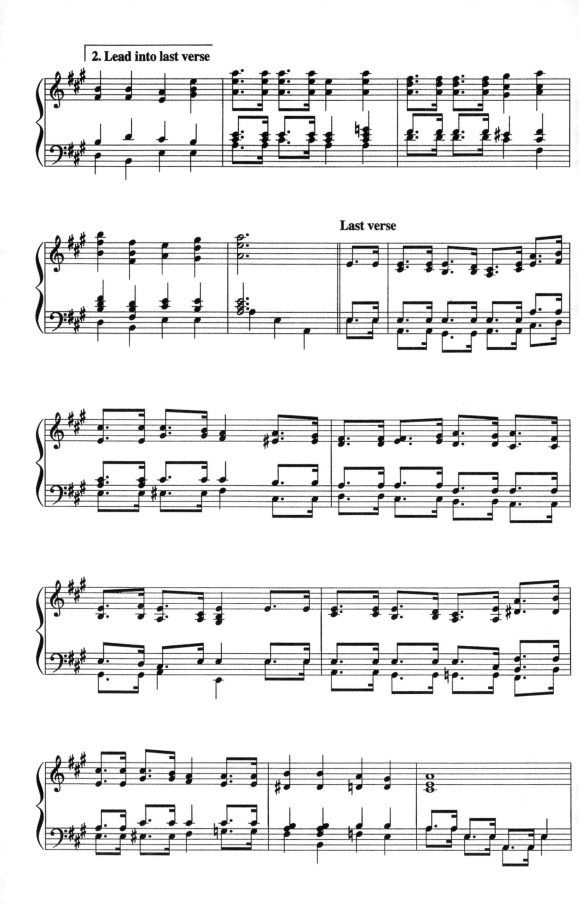

2. Lead into last verse

Last verse

Refrain

Conclusion

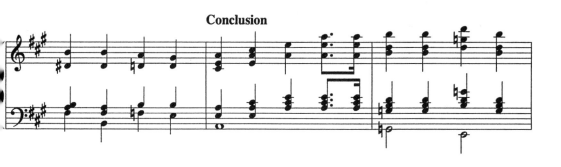

Metre: 14 15 15 6 and Refrain
Melody: Traditional American

10 BELMONT

Introduction

𝄋 Verses

1. D.S. for more verses

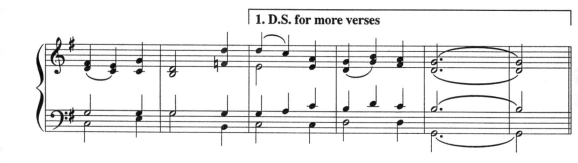

2. Lead into last verse

Last verse

Conclusion

Metre: 86 86 (CM)
Melody: Adapted from William Gardiner's *Sacred Melodies* (1815)

11 BILLING

Last verse

a tempo

Conclusion

Metre: 86 86 (CM)
Melody: Richard Runciman Terry (1865-1938)

12 BLAENWERN

Introduction

℅ Verses

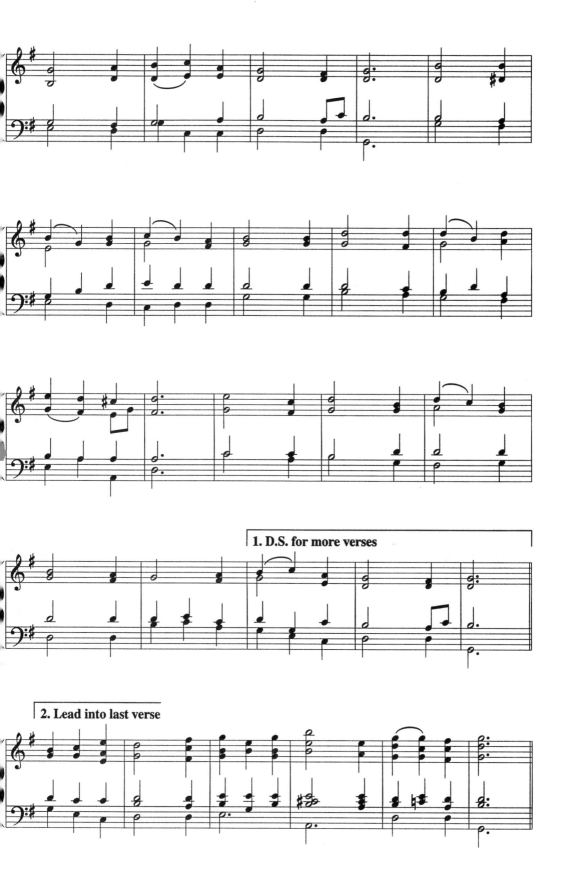

1. D.S. for more verses

2. Lead into last verse

Last verse

Conclusion

Metre: 87 87 D
Melody: William Rowlands (1860-1937)

35

13 BROTHER JAMES'S AIR

Last verse

Conclusion

Metre: 86 86 (CM)
Melody: Brother Leith MacBeth Bain (c. 1860-1925)

14 BUCKLAND

Introduction

𝄋 Verses

1. D.S. for more vs.

2. Lead into last verse

Last verse

Conclusion

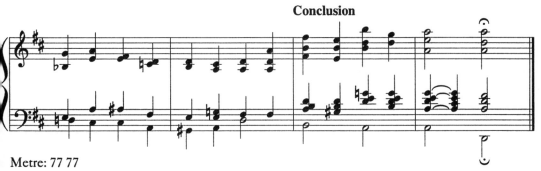

Metre: 77 77
Melody: Leighton George Hayne (1836-1883)

39

15 BUNESSAN

Introduction

℅ Verses

1. D.S. for more vs. | **2. Lead into last verse**

Last verse

Conclusion

Metre: 55 54 D
Melody: Traditional Gaelic

16 CARLISLE

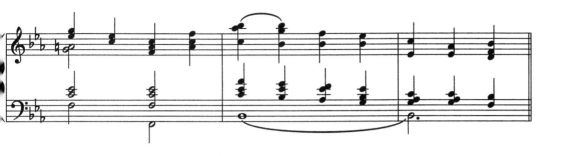

Last verse

Conclusion

Metre: 66 86 (SM)
Melody: Charles Lockhart (1745-1815)

17 CASWALL

Introduction

℁ Verses

1. D.S. for more verses | **2. Lead into last verse**

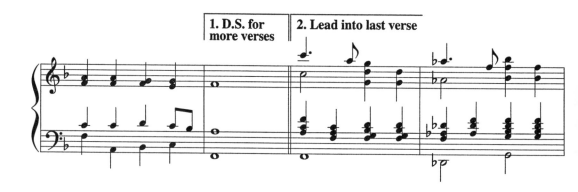

Last verse
a tempo

molto rit.

Conclusion

Metre: 65 65
Melody: Friedrich Filitz (1804-1876)

18 CHORUS ANGELORUM

2. Lead into last verse

Last verse

Conclusion

Metre: 86 86 (CM)
Melody: Arthur Somervell (1863-1937)

47

19 CRADLE SONG

Introduction

Last verse

Conclusion

Metre: 11 11 11 11
Melody: William James Kirkpatrick (1838-1921)

49

20 CRANHAM

Introduction

Verses

1. D.S. for more vs.

2. Lead into last verse

Last verse

Conclusion

Metre: Irregular
Melody: Gustav Holst (1874-1934)

21 CRIMOND

Introduction

𝄋 **Verses**

1. D.S. for more verses

2. Lead into last verse

Metre: 86 86 (CM)
Melody: Jessie Seymour Irvine (1836-1887)

22 CRÜGER

Introduction

𝄋 **Verses**

1. D.S. for more verses

Metre: 76 76 D
Melody: Johann Crüger (1598-1662) adapted by William Henry Monk (1823-1889)

23 CULBACH

Introduction

𝄋 Verses

1. D.S. for more verses

2. Lead into last verse

Last verse

Conclusion

Metre: 77 77
Melody: Adapted from Johann Scheffler's *Heilige Seelenlust* (1657)

24 CWM RHONDDA

Metre: 87 87 47
Melody: John Hughes (1873-1932)

25 DARWALL'S 148th

2. Lead into last verse

Tuba

Last verse

Conclusion

Metre: 66 66 44 44
Melody: John Darwall (1731-1789)

26 DIADEMATA

2. Lead into last verse

Last verse

Conclusion

Metre: 66 86 D (DSM)
Melody: George Job Elvey (1816-1893)

27 DIX

Last verse

Conclusion

Metre: 77 77 77
Melody: Conrad Kocher (1786-1872)

28 DOMINUS REGIT ME

2. Lead into last verse

Last verse

Conclusion

Metre: 87 87
Melody: John Bacchus Dykes (1823-1876)

29 EASTER HYMN

Last verse

Conclusion

Metre: 77 77 and Alleluias
Melody: From *Lyra Davidica* (1708)

30 ELLACOMBE

2. Lead into last verse

Last verse

Conclusion

Tuba

Tuba

Metre: 76 76 D
Melody: From *Württemberg Gesangbuch* (1784)

71

31 EVELYNS

Last verse

Conclusion

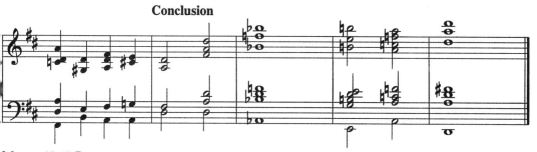

Metre: 65 65 D
Melody: William Henry Monk (1823-1889)

32 EVENTIDE

Introduction

Verses

1. D.S. for more vs.

2. Lead into last verse

molto rit.

Last verse
a tempo

Conclusion

Metre: 10 10 10 10
Melody: William Henry Monk (1823-1889)

33 EWING

Last verse

Conclusion

Metre: 76 76 D
Melody: Alexander Ewing (1830-1895)

34 FULDA

Metre: 88 88 (LM)
Melody: From William Gardiner's *Sacred Melodies* (1815)

35 GERONTIUS

Introduction

℠ **Verses**

1. D.S. for more verses **2. Lead into last verse**

Last verse

Conclusion

Metre: 86 86 (CM)
Melody: John Bacchus Dykes (1823-1876)

36 GOPSAL

Last verse

Conclusion

Metre: 66 66 88
Melody: George Frideric Handel (1685-1759)

37 GWALCHMAI

2. Lead into last verse

molto rit.

Last verse
a tempo

Conclusion

Metre: 74 74 D
Melody: Joseph David Jones (1827-1870)

85

38 HANOVER

Introduction

𝄊 **Verses**

1. D.S. for more verses ‖ **2. Lead into last verse**

Last verse

Conclusion

Metre: 10 10 11 11
Melody: William Croft (1678-1727)

39 HELMSLEY

Introduction

𝄋 Verses

1. D.S. for more verses

2. Lead into last verse

Last verse

Conclusion

Metre: 87 87 47
Melody: From John Wesley's *Select Hymns* (1765)

40 HIGHWOOD

2. Lead into last verse

Last verse

Conclusion

Metre: 11 10 11 10
Melody: Richard Runciman Terry (1865-1938)

93

41 HORSLEY

2. Lead into last verse

Last verse

Conclusion

Metre: 86 86 (CM)
Melody: William Horsley (1774-1858)

95

42 HYFRYDOL

Introduction

1. D.S. for more verses

2. Lead into last verse

Last verse

Conclusion

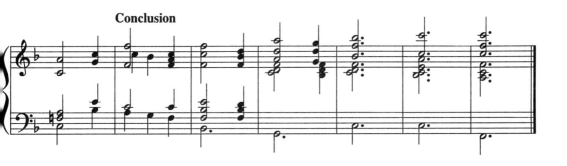

Metre: 87 87 D
Melody: Rowland Huw Pritchard (1811-1887)

43 IRBY

Metre: 87 87 77

Melody: Henry John Gauntlett (1805-1876)

44 LASST UNS ERFREUEN

2. Lead into last verse

Tuba

Last verse

Refrain

Conclusion

Metre: 88 44 88 and Alleluias
Melody: From *Geistliche Kirchengesang*, Cologne (1623)

45 LAUDATE DOMINUM

Metre: 10 10 11 11
Melody: Hubert Parry (1848-1918)

46 LAUS DEO (Redhead No. 46)

Last verse

Conclusion

Metre: 87 87
Melody: Richard Redhead (1820-1901)

109

47 LEONI

Introduction

℁ **Verses**

1. **D.S. for more verses**

2. Lead into last verse

Last verse

Conclusion

Metre: 66 84 D
Melody: Traditional Hebrew

48 LLANFAIR

Metre: 77 77 and Alleluias
Melody: Robert Williams (1781-1821)

49 LOBE DEN HERREN

Last verse

Conclusion

Metre: 14 14 4 7 8
Melody: From *Praxis Pietatis Melica* (1668)

50 LOVE DIVINE

Last verse

a tempo

Conclusion

Metre: 87 87
Melody: John Stainer (1840-1901)

51 MACCABAEUS

Metre: 10 11 11 11 and Refrain
Melody: George Frideric Handel (1685-1759)

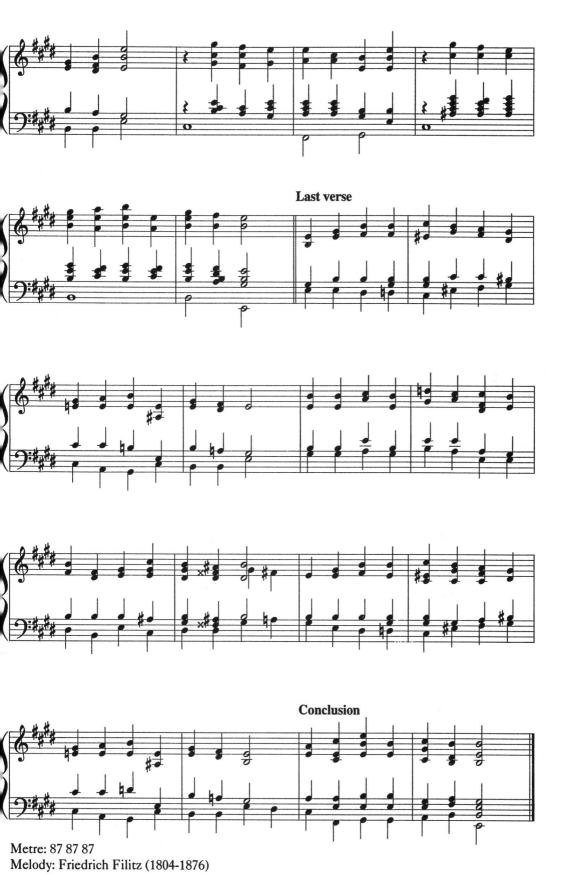

Last verse

Conclusion

Metre: 87 87 87
Melody: Friedrich Filitz (1804-1876)

53 MELCOMBE

2. Lead into last verse

Last verse

Conclusion

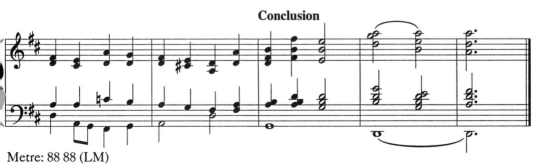

Metre: 88 88 (LM)
Melody: Samuel Webbe (1740-1816)

54 MELITA

Introduction

Verses

1. D.S. for more verses

2. Lead into last verse

Last verse

Conclusion

Metre: 88 88 88
Melody: John Bacchus Dykes (1823-1876)

55 MENDELSSOHN

2. Lead into last verse

Last verse

Refrain

Conclusion

Metre: 77 77 D 77
Melody: Felix Mendelssohn (1809-1847)

56 MILES LANE

Introduction

𝄋 Verses

1. D.S. for more verses | **2. Lead into last verse**

Metre: 86 86 (CM)
Melody: William Shrubsole (1760-1806)

57 MONKLAND

2. Lead into last verse

Last verse

Refrain

Conclusion

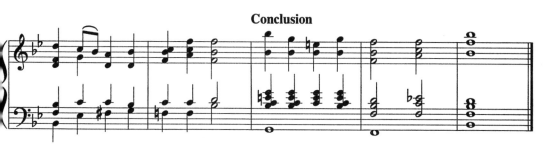

Metre: 77 77
Melody: John Antes (1740-1811)

58 MOSCOW

Last verse

Conclusion

Metre: 664 66 64
Melody: Felice de Giardini (1716-1796)

59 NARENZA

2. Lead into last verse

Last verse

Conclusion

Metre: 66 86 (SM)
Melody: From Leisentritt's *Catholicum Hymnologium Germanicum* (1584)
adapted by William Henry Havergal (1793-1870)

60 NICAEA

Introduction

Metre: 11 12 12 10
Melody: John Bacchus Dykes (1823-1876)

137

61 NOEL NOUVELET

Metre: 11 11 10 11
Melody: Traditional French

62 NUN DANKET

2. Lead into last verse

Last verse

Conclusion

Metre: 67 67 66 66
Melody: Johann Crüger (1598-1662)

141

63 OLD HUNDREDTH

Introduction

Tuba

℁ **Verses**

1. **D.S.**
for more vs.

2. Lead into last verse

Last verse

Conclusion

Metre: 88 88 (LM)
Melody: From the *Genevan Psalter* (1551)

143

64 PADERBORN

Metre: 10 10 11 11
Melody: From *Paderborn Gesangbuch* (1765)

65 PASSION CHORALE

Last verse

Conclusion

Metre: 76 76 D
Melody: Hans Leo Hassler (1564-1612)

147

66 PERSONENT HODIE

148

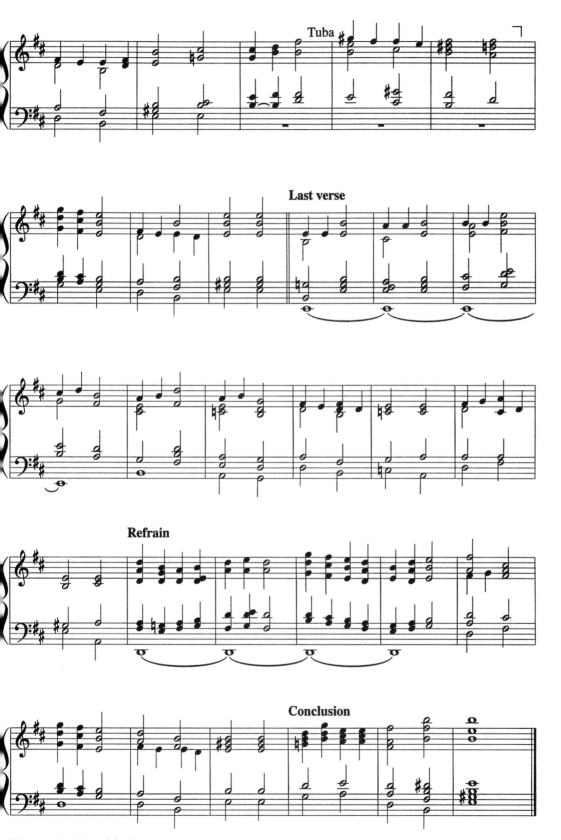

Metre: 666 66 and Refrain
Melody: From *Piae Cantiones* (1582)

67 PICARDY

Last verse

Conclusion

Metre: 87 87 87
Melody: Traditional French carol

68 PRAISE MY SOUL

Last verse

Conclusion

Metre: 87 87 87
Melody: John Goss (1800-1880)

69 REGENT SQUARE

Metre: 87 87 87
Melody: Henry Smart (1813-1879)

70 REPTON

2. Lead into last verse

Last verse

Conclusion

Metre: 86 88 6
Melody: Hubert Parry (1848-1918)

157

71 RICHMOND

Introduction

% **Verses**

1. D.S. for more verses

158

2. Lead into last verse

Last verse

Conclusion

Metre: 86 86 (CM)
Melody: Thomas Haweis (1734-1820)

72 ROCKINGHAM

Introduction

2. Lead into last verse

Last verse

Conclusion

Metre: 88 88 (LM)
Melody: Adapted by Edward Miller (1735-1807)

161

73 ROYAL OAK

2. Lead into last verse

Last verse

Refrain

Conclusion

Metre: 76 76 and Refrain
Melody: Traditional English

163

74 SAFFRON WALDEN

Last verse

Conclusion

Metre: 88 86
Melody: Arthur Henry Brown (1830-1926)

165

75 ST BERNARD

Last verse

Conclusion

Metre: 86 86 (CM)
Melody: Adapted from *Tochter Sion* (1741)

Introduction

℠ **Verses**

1. D.S. for more verses

2. Lead into last verse

Last verse

Conclusion

Metre: 98 98
Melody: Clement Cotterill Scholefield (1839-1904)

169

77 ST COLUMBA

Last verse

Conclusion

Metre: 87 87
Melody: Traditional Irish

171

78 ST DENIO

Introduction

℈ Verses

1. D.S. for more verses

2. Lead into last verse

Metre: 11 11 11 11
Melody: Traditional Welsh from John Roberts' *Caniadau y Cyssegre* (1839)

79 ST FULBERT

Introduction

𝄋 Verses

| 1. D.S. for more vs. | 2. Lead into last verse |

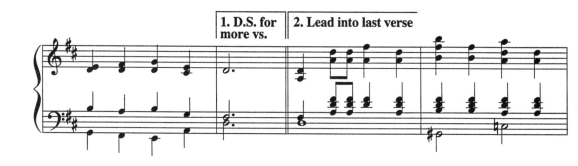

174

Last verse

Conclusion

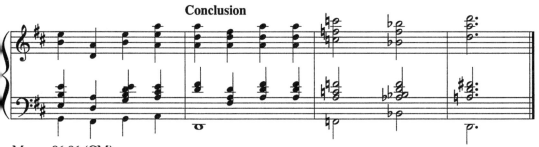

Metre: 86 86 (CM)
Melody: Henry John Gauntlett (1805-1876)

80 ST THEODULPH

1. D.S. for refrain and verses

2. Lead into last refrain

Last refrain

Conclusion

Metre: 76 76 D
Melody: Melchior Teschner (1584-1635)

81 ST THOMAS (Webbe)

Introduction

𝄋 Verses

1. D.S. for more verses

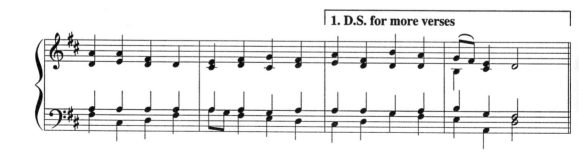

2. Lead into last verse

Last verse

Conclusion

Metre: 87 87 87
Melody: Samuel Webbe (1740-1816)

82 ST THOMAS (Williams)

Last verse

Conclusion

Metre: 66 86 (SM)
Melody: Aaron Williams (1731-1776)

83 SALZBURG

2. Lead into last verse

molto rit.

Last verse
a tempo

Conclusion

Metre: 77 77 D
Melody: Jacob Hintze (1622-1702)

84 SANDYS

Last verse

Conclusion

Metre: 66 86 (SM)
Melody: From William Sandys' *Christmas Carols* (1833)

85 SING HOSANNA

2. Lead into last verse

Metre: 10 8 10 9 and Refrain
Melody: Traditional

86 SLANE

2. Lead into last verse

Last verse

Conclusion

Metre: 10 11 11 11
Melody: Traditional Irish

87   SONG 34 (Angels' Song)

Last verse

Conclusion

Metre: 88 88 (LM)
Melody: Orlando Gibbons (1583-1625)

88 STILLE NACHT

Introduction

℁ Verses

1. D.S. for more verses

2. Lead into last verse

Last verse

Conclusion

Metre: Irregular
Melody: Franz Grüber (1787-1863)

89 STRENGTH AND STAY

2. Lead into last verse

Last verse

Conclusion

Metre: 11 10 11 10
Melody: John Bacchus Dykes (1823-1876)

90 STUTTGART

196

Metre: 87 87
Melody: Christian Friedrich Witt (1660-1716)

91 SURREY

Metre: 88 88 88
Melody: Henry Carey (c.1690-1743)

199

92 TALLIS'S CANON

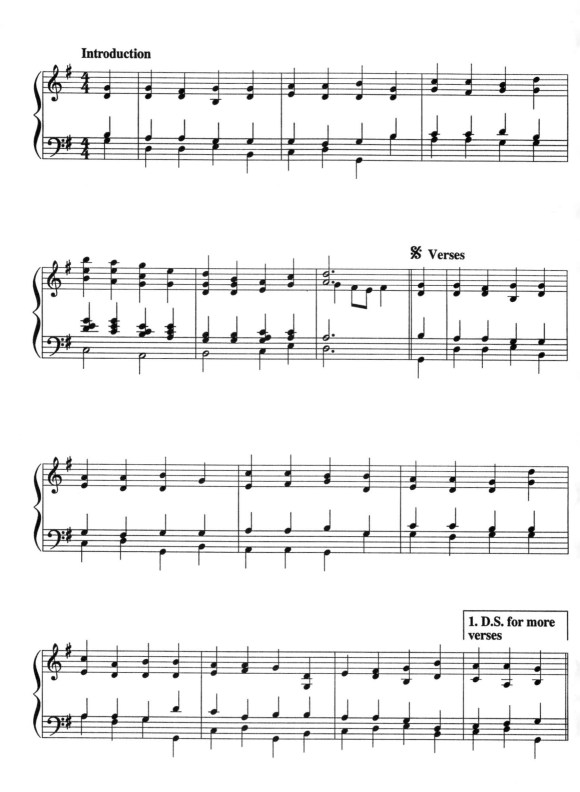

Last verse

Conclusion

Metre: 88 88 (LM)
Melody: Thomas Tallis (c.1505-1585)

93 TALLIS'S ORDINAL

Last verse

Conclusion

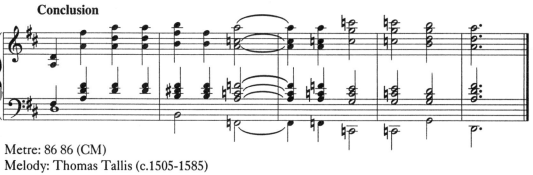

Metre: 86 86 (CM)
Melody: Thomas Tallis (c.1505-1585)

94 THE FIRST NOWELL

Refrain

1. D.S. for more verses **2. Lead into last verse**

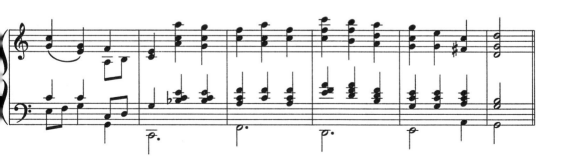

Last verse

Refrain

Conclusion

Metre: Irregular
Melody: Traditional English carol

95 THIS JOYFUL EASTERTIDE

1. D.S. for more verses　　　**2. Lead into last verse**

Tuba

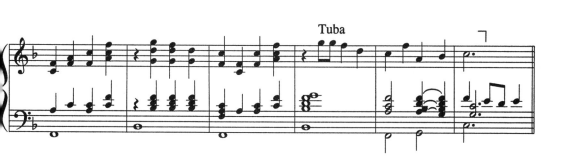

Last verse

Refrain

Conclusion

Tuba

Metre: 67 67 and Refrain
Melody: From *David's Psalmen*, Amsterdam (1685)

96 WAREHAM

Introduction

Verses

1. D.S. for more verses

2. Lead into last verse

Last verse

Conclusion

Metre: 88 88 (LM)
Melody: William Knapp (1698-1768)

97 WAS LEBET

214

Metre: 13 10 13 10
Melody: From *Rheinhardt MS* (1754)

98 WESTMINSTER ABBEY

Metre: 87 87 87
Melody: Henry Purcell (1659-1695)

99 WINCHESTER NEW

Last verse

Conclusion

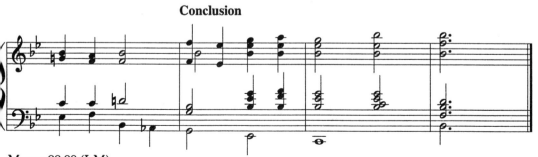

Metre: 88 88 (LM)
Melody: *Musikalisches Hand-Buch* (1690)

100 WIR PFLÜGEN

Metre: 76 76 D and Refrain
Melody: Johann Abraham Peter Schulz (1747-1800)

Metrical Index